MY GIANT DEADLY DINOSAURS

Ultimate Sticker and Activity Fun

igloobooks

CLOSE ENCOUNTER

This herd of Megalosaurus (MEG-UH-LOW-SAWR-US) are hunting their prey. Which of these images is the odd one out?

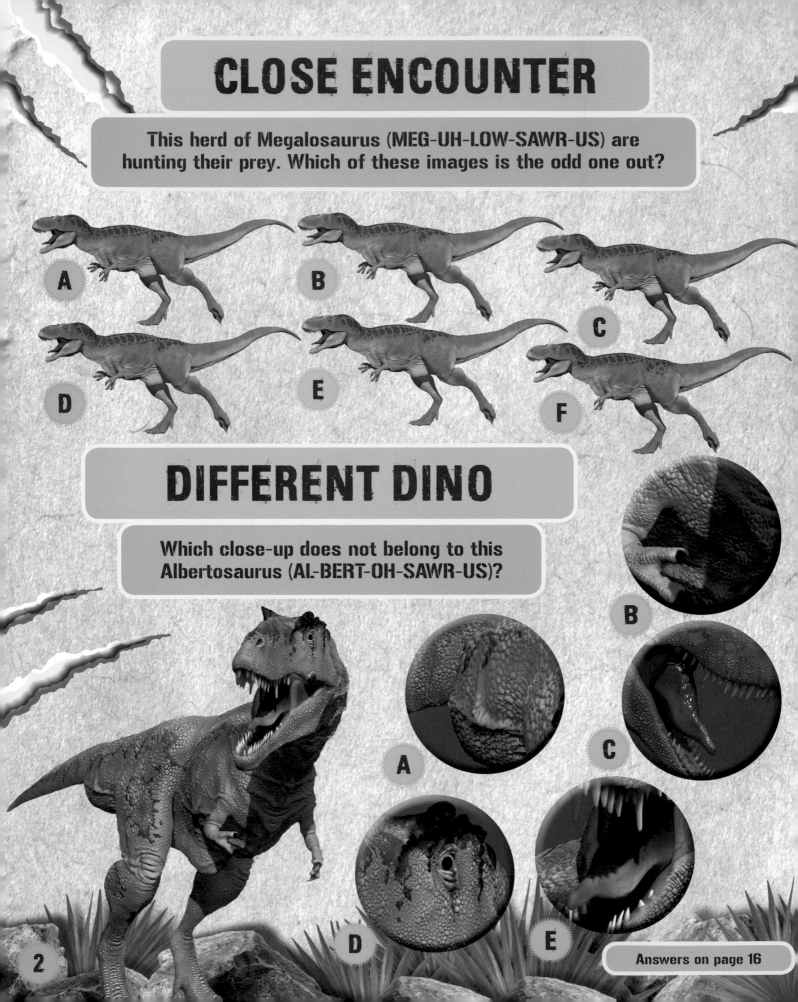

A B C D E F

DIFFERENT DINO

Which close-up does not belong to this Albertosaurus (AL-BERT-OH-SAWR-US)?

A B C D E

Answers on page 16

ALLOSAURUS
(AL-OH-SAWR-US)

Period: Jurassic
203–135 million years ago

HEIGHT: 5m (17ft)
LENGTH: 12m (40ft)
WEIGHT: 1814kg (4000lbs)

FOOTPRINT PUZZLER

A Ceratosaurus (SIH-RAT-OH-SAWR-US) has trampled on this puzzle. Match each of the missing pieces to the correct gap in the picture.

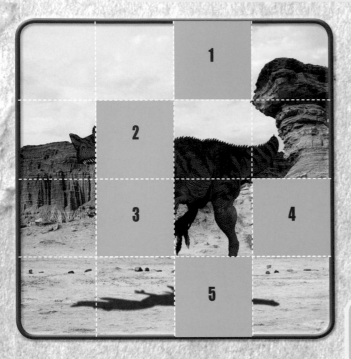

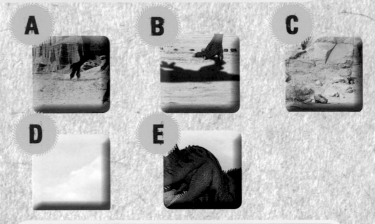

A

B

C

D

E

ROAR DRAW

Copy the picture of this awesome Giganotosaurus (GIG-AH-NO-TOE-SAWR-US) into the grid below.

Answers on page 16

TYRANNOSAURUS LUNCH

This Tyrannosaurus (TIE-RAN-OH-SAWR-US) is making short work of his prey. Which detail does not appear in the scene?

A

B

C

D

E

F

DINO DRAW

Follow these step-by-step instructions to draw an amazing Megalosaurus (MEG-UH-LOW-SAWR-US).

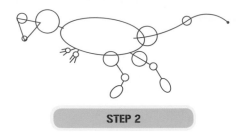

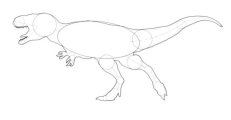

STEP 2

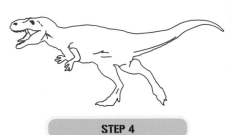

STEP 4

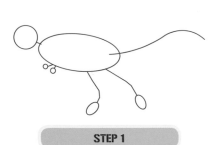

STEP 1

STEP 3

TYRANNOSAURUS
(TIE-RAN-OH-SAWR-US)

Period: Jurassic
203–135 million years ago

HEIGHT: 7m (27ft)

LENGTH: 15m (50ft)

WEIGHT: 6350kg (14,000lbs)

SPOT THE DIFFERENCE

This Tarbosaurus (TARB-UH-SAWR-US) is hunting its prey. Circle the five differences between the two pictures.

CARNOTAURUS TRAIL

This Carnotaurus (CAR-NO-TORE-US) is searching for food. Which trail will lead it to the Iguanodon (IG-WAH-NA-DON)?

8

Answers on page 16

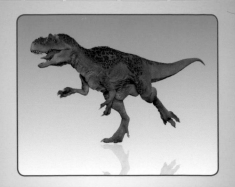

ALLOSAURUS

HEIGHT: 5m (17ft)

WEIGHT: 1814kg (3999lbs)

FEROCITY `9`

The Allosaurus once inhabited what is now North America. Dozens of complete fossils have been found in quarries and other areas.

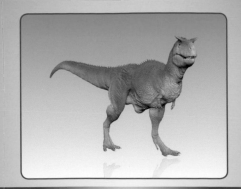

CERATOSAUR

HEIGHT: 2.5m (8ft)

WEIGHT: 1359kg (2996lbs)

FEROCITY `8`

Unlike most similar predators, the Ceratosaur feasted on fish as well as other dinosaurs.

GIGANOTOSAURUS

HEIGHT: 7m (23ft)

WEIGHT: 8800kg (19,400lbs)

FEROCITY `4`

Giganotosaurus hunted in packs, taking down huge dinosaurs in groups of three or four.

ALBERTOSAURUS

HEIGHT: 2.5m (8ft)

WEIGHT: 1724kg (3801lbs)

FEROCITY `6`

This dinosaur is closely related to the T-Rex and preyed on small herbivores.

CARNOTAURUS

HEIGHT: 3m (10ft)

WEIGHT: 2087kg (4601lbs)

FEROCITY `6`

This dinosaur was a huge creature but thanks to its very straight tail, it was able to reach high speeds.

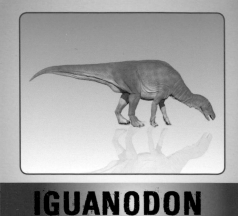

IGUANODON

HEIGHT: 3m (10ft)

WEIGHT: 3175kg (7000lbs)

FEROCITY `3`

Iguanodon fossils have been discovered all over the world - in Asia, Europe and North America.

HOW TO PLAY:

Top Trumps

1. Shuffle and divide the cards between two players. Each player must hold their cards face up in a pile in their hands, only looking at the top card.

2. Player one must read out an item from his/her top card (e.g. Ferocity 8). Player two must then read out the same item on his/her top card.

3. The player with the highest value wins and gets to take the other player's card.

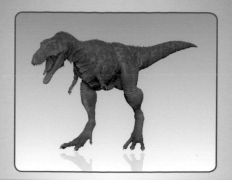

TARBOSAURUS

HEIGHT: 3.5m (11.5ft)

WEIGHT: 4536kg (10,000lbs)

FEROCITY `7`

Tarbosaurus was a deadly predator but often scavenged food from already dead dinosaurs.

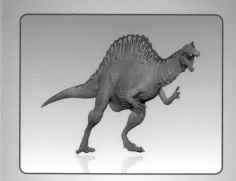

SPINOSAURUS

HEIGHT: 5m (17ft)

WEIGHT: 4000kg (8816lbs)

FEROCITY `9`

The distinctive spine on the back of the Spinosaurus is supported by sharp needles of bone.

UTAHRAPTOR

HEIGHT: 2m (6ft)

WEIGHT: 500kg (1102lbs)

FEROCITY `9`

The Utahraptor had a claw on its hind legs that measured around a foot in length.

VELOCIRAPTOR

HEIGHT: 90cm (3ft)

WEIGHT: 15kg (33lbs)

FEROCITY `8`

The name 'velociraptor' comes from the Greek language and means speedy thief.

TYRANNOSAURUS

HEIGHT: 7m (23ft)

WEIGHT: 6350kg (14,000lbs)

FEROCITY `10`

The Tyrannosaurus Rex is one of the most popular dinosaurs. The name means 'Tyrant Lizard King'.

MEGALOSAURUS

HEIGHT: 3m (10ft)

WEIGHT: 2205 kg (4861lbs)

FEROCITY `7`

Megalosaurus was the first dinosaur ever to be named. Its name means 'Great Lizard'.

4. The winner takes the next turn to read out from his/her next card.

5. If both players read out an equal value, they must place their cards in a pile between them. The next player to win takes all of the cards from that pile, as well as the other player's card.

6. The player with all of the cards at the end of the game is the winner.

2 Players

SPINOSAURUS
SPY-NO-SAWR-US

Period: Jurassic
203–135 million years ago

HEIGHT: 5m (17ft)

LENGTH: 15m (50ft)

WEIGHT: 6350kg (8816lbs)

ROUND-UP RAPTORS

These Utahraptor (YOO-TAH-RAP-TUH) are on the loose.
Round them up by drawing a line between each matching pair.

DINO DOTS

Join the dots on this fearsome Allosaurus
(AL-OH-SAWR-US) and then decorate it with your best pens.

Answers on page 16

GIGANOTOSAURUS
(GIG-AH-NO-TOE-SAWR-US)

Period: Cretaceous
135–65 million years ago
HEIGHT: 7m (23ft)
LENGTH: 15m (46ft)
WEIGHT: 8800kg (19,400lbs)

MEGA MAZE

Help the Tyrannosaurus (TIE-RAN-OH-SAWR-US) get to its dinner by drawing a line through the maze.

START

FINISH

12

Answers on page 16

FIND AND COUNT

How many Velociraptor (VUH-LOSS-UH-RAP-TUH) can you find in this forest scene? Circle each one.

13

IN THE SHADOWS

Which of these shadows matches the frightening
Allosaurus (AL-OH-SAWR-US) exactly?

A

B

C

D

MEAT-EATER MIX-UP

Put these four meat-eaters back together by
drawing a line between two matching halves.

A

B

C

D

1

2

3

4

14

Answers on page 16

MEGALOSAURUS
(MEG-UH-LO-SAWR-US)

Period: Jurassic
203–135 million years ago
HEIGHT: 3m (10ft)
LENGTH: 9m (30ft)
WEIGHT: 1000kg (2205lbs)

ANSWER PAGE

Page 2
Close Encounter: F
Different Dino: C

Page 4
Footprint Puzzler:

1-D
2-E
3-A
4-C
5-B

Page 5
Tyrannosaurus Lunch: C

Page 8
Spot the Difference:

Page 8
Carnotaurus Trail: Route 3

Page 10
Round-Up Raptors: A-L, B-J, C-F, D-H, E-K, G-I

Page 12
Mega Maze:

Page 13
Find and Count: 6 Velociraptors

Page 14
In the Shadows: Allosaurus C
Meat-Eater Mix-Up: A-3, B-4, C-2, D-1

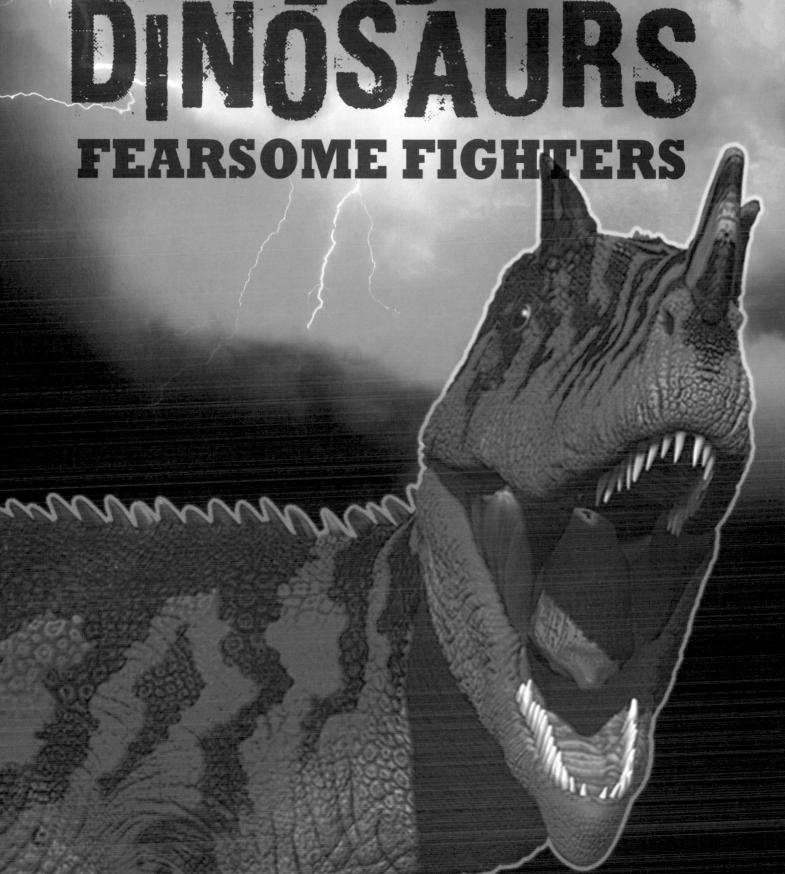

DEADLY DiNoSAURS
FEARSOME FIGHTERS

GIGANOTO-GRID

Follow the clues to get the Giganotosaurus
(GIG-AH-NO-TOE-SAWR-US) through the grid and to his next meal.

CLUES

- Right 5
- Down 2
- Left 3
- Down 2
- Right 1
- Down 1
- Right 3

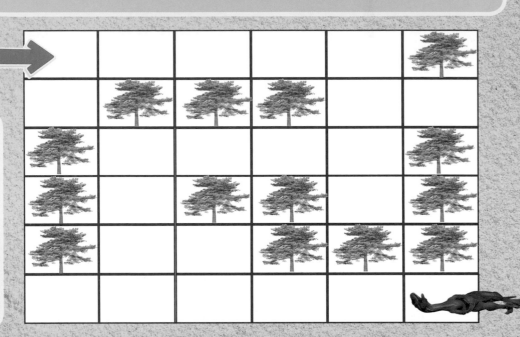

SEEING DOUBLE

Look at these two scenes. Circle the
dinosaur that has appeared in scene B.

A

B

Answers on page 32

BATTLEGROUND

How many of each dinosaur can you spot in this fight scene? Fill in your answers in the boxes below.

Kentrosaurus

Protoceratops

Tyrannosaurus

Stegosaurus

Answers on page 32

ROW OF ROARS

These fearsome fighters appear in the same order on each row.
Use the stickers from your sticker sheet to fill in the gaps.

PUZZLE PIECES

Work out where each piece of the puzzle should go.
Which of the pieces doesn't fit into the picture?

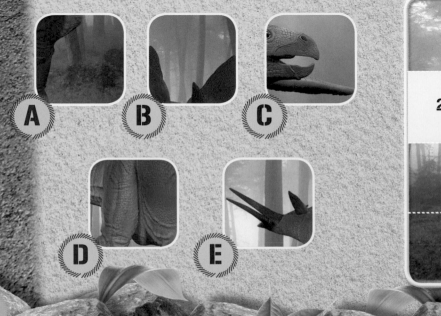

A   **B**   **C**

D   **E**

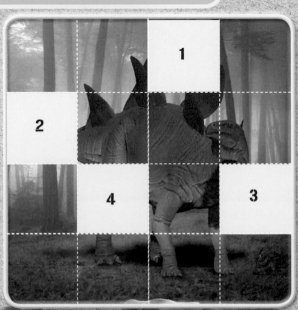

1

2

4   3

Answers on page 32

UTAHRAPTOR
(YOO-TAH-RAP-TOR)

Period: Cretaceous

135–65 million years ago

HEIGHT: 1.5m (6ft)
LENGTH: 6m (20ft)
WEIGHT: 4064kg (8960lbs)

DINO D.I.Y.

These fearsome fighters are missing distinctive features.
Draw a line between each dino and its missing part.

A B C D

1 2 3 4

TERROR TRAIL

This Ankylosaurus (AN-KILE-OH-SAWR-US) has been seperated from the
herd. Draw a line through the maze to help it find its way back to them.

START

FINISH

22

Answers on page 32

SCENE IT

This is an awesome scene of a Ceratosaurus (SIH-RAT-OH-SAWR-US). Which of the images below isn't in the scene?

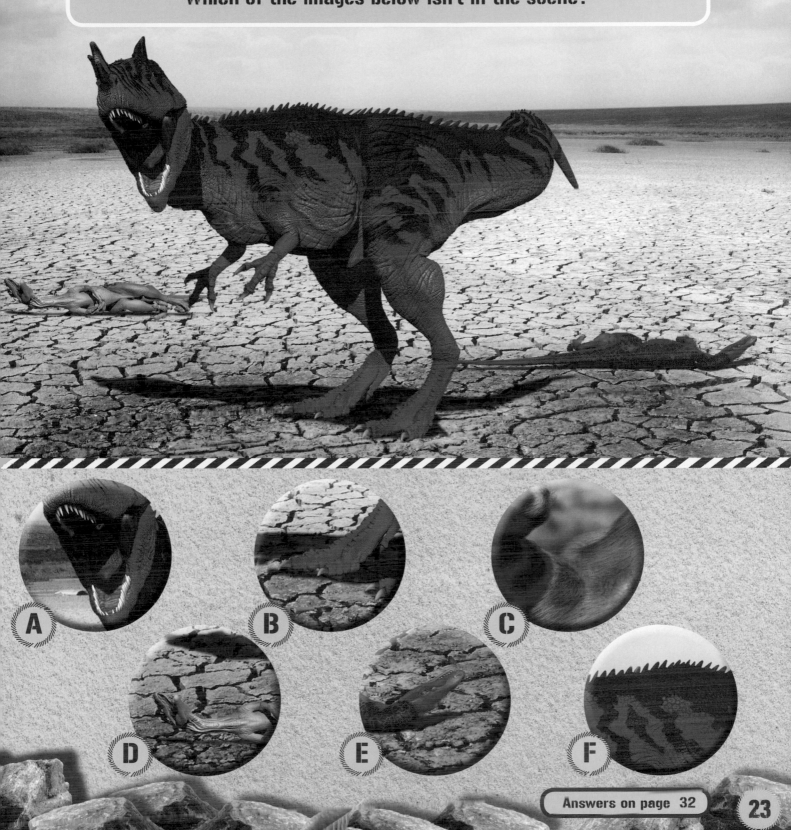

A

B

C

D

E

F

Answers on page 32

MEMORY TEST

Look at this scene of a ferocious Albertosaurus (AL-BERT-OH-SAWR-US) for 30 seconds. Now turn to page 26 and answer the questions.

ALBERTOSAURUS

Terrifying T-Rex

Push out all the pieces of the T-Rex and the stand. Push the tabs on the head and tail firmly. Slot the head and tail pieces into the body piece and secure with sticky tape. Fold the stand into a v-shape and place the slots at the base of the T-Rex into the slots in the base.

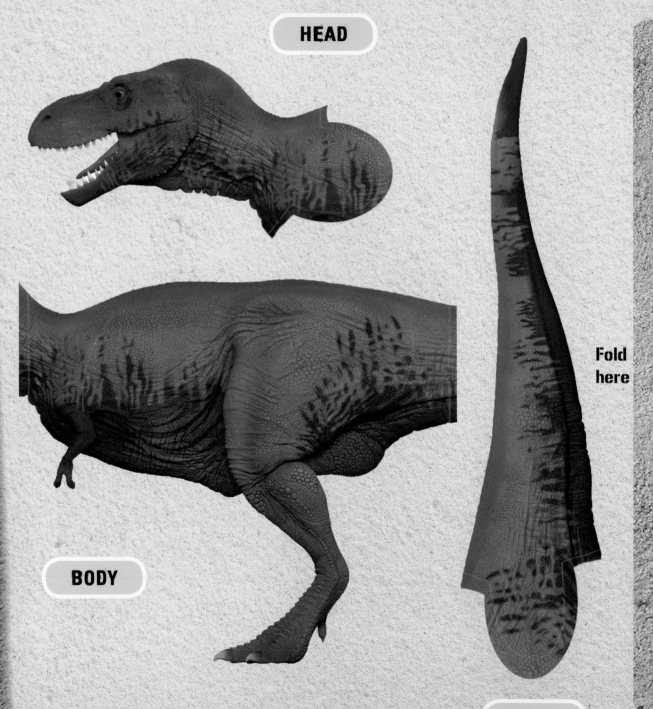

STAND

HEAD

Fold here

BODY

TAIL

Tenacious Triceratops

TAIL

Push out all the pieces of the Triceratops and the stand.
Push the tabs on the head and tail firmly. Slot the head and tail
pieces into the body piece and secure with sticky tape.
Fold the stand into a v-shape and place the slots at the base
of the Triceratops into the slots in the base.

Fold
here

BODY

HEAD

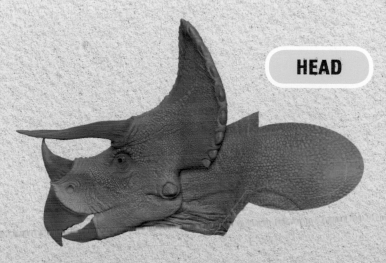

STAND

TRICERATOPS
(TRY-SEH-RA-TOPS)

Period: Cretaceous
135–65 million years ago

HEIGHT: 3m (9ft)
LENGTH: 11m (33ft)
WEIGHT:11,000kg(24,250lbs)

MEMORY TEST QUESTIONS

Look at the illustration of the ferocious Albertosaurus (AL-BERT-OH-SAWR-US) on page 24 for 30 seconds and then answer these true-or-false questions.

1. There are four claws on each foot of the Albertosaurus.
2. The Albertosaurus is chasing three small dinosaurs.
3. The Albertosaurus' prey have blue stripes on their back.
4. There are yellow patches of skin on the Albertosaurus' back.

DINOSAUR-DOKU

Use the stickers from your sticker sheet to complete this grid so that there is only one of each dinosaur in each row and column.

COLUMNS

ROWS

Answers on page 32

ANKYLOSAURUS
(AN-KILE-OH-SAWR-US)

Period: Cretaceous
135–65 million years ago

HEIGHT: 1.5m (5ft)
LENGTH: 8m (24ft)
WEIGHT: 3556kg (7840lbs)

TYRANNOSAURUS CHASE

This Ankylosaurus is being chased by a ferocious T-Rex. Help it escape across the plateau and towards the jungle where it can hide.

How to Play

One player takes the role of the T-Rex and the other takes the role of the Ankylosaurus. Find the stickers on your sticker sheet and stick them to a coin. The Ankylosaurus rolls the dice twice and moves their piece the correct amount of squares. The T-Rex then rolls the dice and the two players then take turns. The game ends when the Ankylosaurus reaches the jungle or the T-Rex lands on the square that the Ankylosaurus is on.

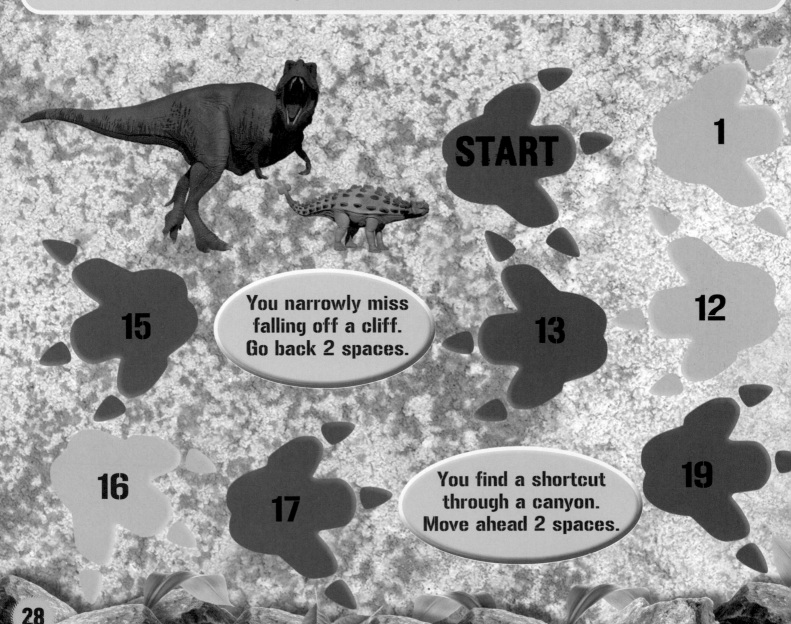

START

1

15

You narrowly miss falling off a cliff. Go back 2 spaces.

13

12

16

17

You find a shortcut through a canyon. Move ahead 2 spaces.

19

TRI AGAIN

Draw lines between these Triceratops (TRY-SEH-RA-TOPS) to form four matching pairs.

A B C D

E F G H

MATCHING HALVES

Draw a line between these dinosaur halves to make six terrifying fighters.

A B C D E F

1 2 3 4 5 6

Answers on page 32

STEGOSAURUS
(STEG-OH-SAWR-US)

Period: Jurassic
203-135 million years ago

HEIGHT: 5m (14ft)
LENGTH: 11m (36ft)
WEIGHT: 5000kg (11,020lbs)

ANSWER PAGE

Page 18
Giganoto-Grid:

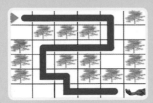

Seeing Double:

Page 19
Battleground:
2 Kentrosaurus, 6 Protoceratops,
4 Tyrannosaurus, 5 Stegosaurus

Page 20
Row of Roars:

Puzzle Pieces:

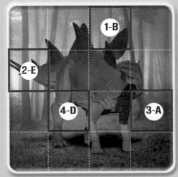

Odd one out is C

Page 22
Dino D.I.Y.:
A-4, B-1, C-2, D-3

Terror Trail:

Page 23
Scene It:
Image C

Page 26
Memory Test Questions
1 - True, 2 - False, 3 - False, 4 - True

Dinosaur-Doku

Page 30
Tri Again
A-G, B-H, C-F, D-E

Matching Halves
A-5, B-4, C-3, D-2, E-6, F-1

DEADLY DINOSAURS
DEEP SEA MONSTERS

OCEAN ODDITIES

Which of these Dunkleosteus
(DUNK-LEE-OH-STEE-US) is the odd one out?

A B C
D E F

JIGSAW JUMBLE

Complete this jigsaw of a prehistoric marine
monster. Which piece doesn't fit the puzzle?

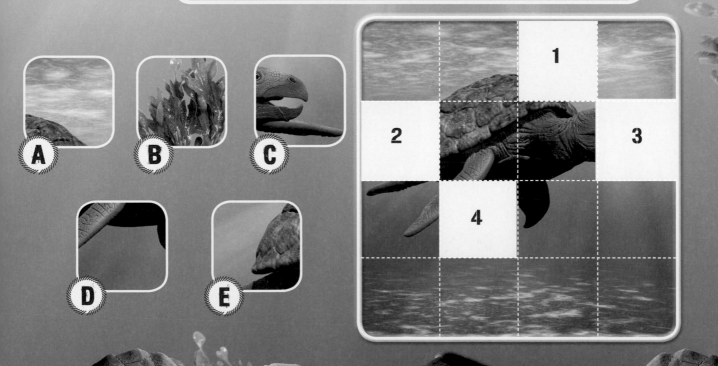

A B C
D E

1

2 3

4

Answers on page 48

BASILOSAURUS
(BASS-IL-OH-SAWR-US)

Period: Jurassic
203–135 million years ago

HEIGHT: 5m (17ft)
LENGTH: 12m (40ft)
WEIGHT: 1814kg (4000lbs)

LIOPLEURODON SHADOWS

Which of these deep-sea shadows matches the menacing Liopleurodon (LIE-OH-PLOOR-UH-DON)?

C

B

A

D

CREATURE CLOSE-UP

A

Match each of these deep-sea creatures to the correct close-up.

B

C

D

1

2

3

4

Answers on page 48

MAUISAURUS
(MOW-EE-SAWR-US)

Period: Cretaceous
135–65 million years ago

HEIGHT: 2m (6ft)
LENGTH: 17m (55ft)
WEIGHT: 9072kg (20,000lbs)

MEGALODON MAZE

Help the Megalodon (MEG-AH-LUH-DON) find its way through the prehistoric coral reef so that it can find its lunch.

START

FINISH

Answers on page 48

FACT FILE

GIANT MOSASAUR
(JI-UNT MOH-SUH-SAWR)

Period: Cretaceous
135–65 million years ago

HEIGHT: 4m (13ft)
LENGTH: 17m (55ft)
WEIGHT: 13,610kg (30,000lbs)

GRUESOME GRID

Copy this picture of a Helicoprion
(HEL-EE-COPE-REE-ON) into the empty grid below.

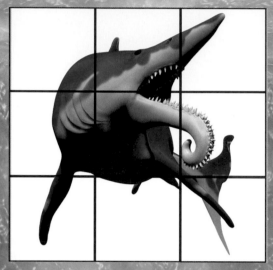

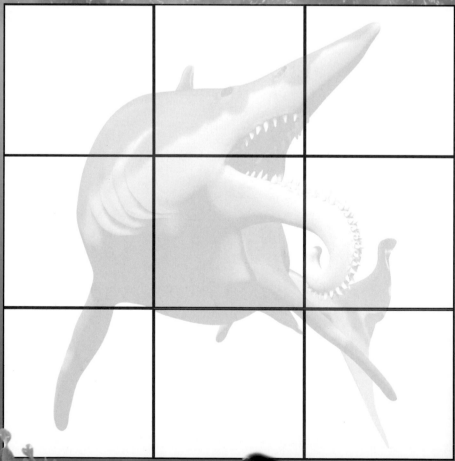

Mega Megalodon

Push out all the pieces of the Megalodon and the stand.
Push the tabs on the head and tail firmly. Slot the head and tail
pieces into the body piece and secure with sticky tape.
Fold the stand into a v-shape and place the slots at the base of
the Megalodon into the slots in the base.

HEAD

BODY

STAND

Fold
here

TAIL

Deep-Sea Monsters

Press out all the pieces carefully. Fold the stand into a v-shape and place the slots at the of the bottom of the deep-sea monster into the slots of the stand.

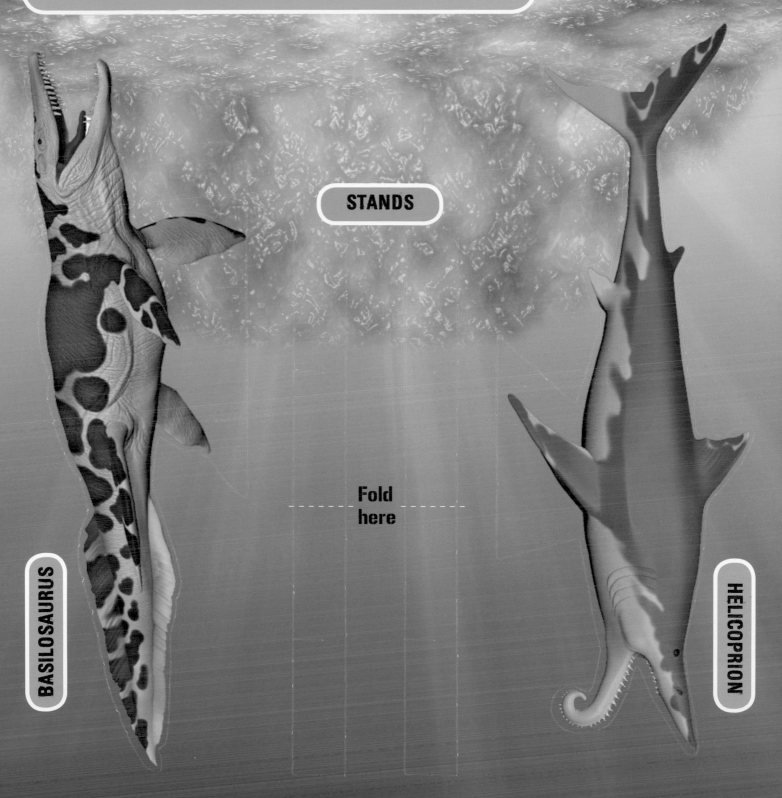

STANDS

Fold here

BASILOSAURUS

HELICOPRION

DEEP-SEA MEMORY TEST

Study this scene for 30 seconds and then answer the questions on page 42.

ELASMOSAURUS

DUNKLEOSTEUS

MEMORY TEST QUESTIONS

Study the scene on page 41 for 30 seconds and then answer these true-or-false questions.

1. There are three types of deep-sea monster in the scene.
2. Two of the creatures are swimming away into the distance.
3. The Dunkleosteus has a stripy red pattern on its back.
4. The Elasmosaurus has a long, orange body.

DOUBLE TROUBLE

Match up these pairs of Megalodon (MEG-AH-LUH-DON) Which of them doesn't have a pair?

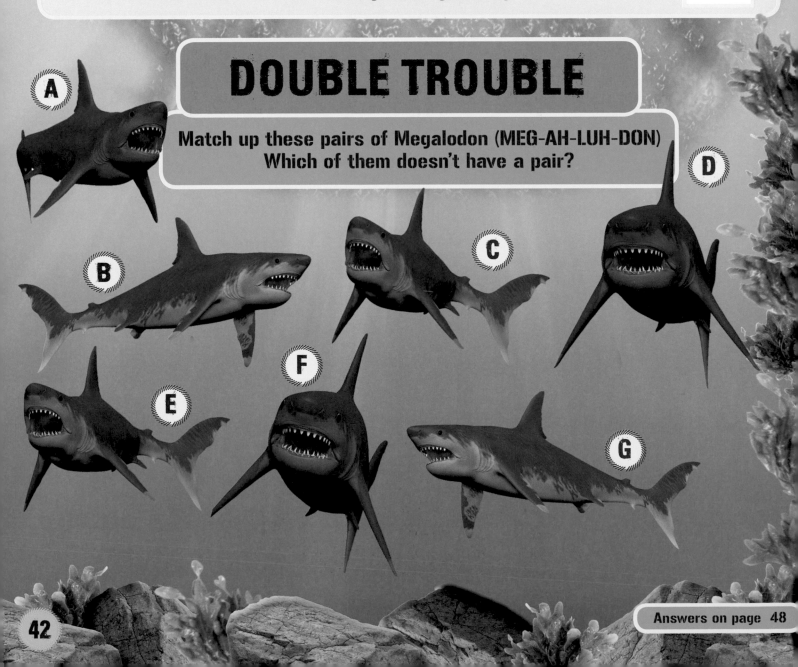

Answers on page 48

FIND AND COUNT

How many deep-sea monsters can you see in this picture? Write your answers in the boxes below.

Dunkleosteus

Megalodon

Sea Scorpion

Answers on page 48

43

DEEP-SEA CREATURES GAME

Help your deep-sea creature race across the sea and get to the end first.

How to Play

1. Each player chooses a sticker from the sticker sheet and sticks it to a coin.
2. Players take it in turn to roll a dice and move their counter around the board.
3. If players land on a Mauisaurus, they can move forward two spaces. If players land on a Megalodon, they must move backwards two spaces.
4. The winner is the first person to reach the finish.

START → 1 → MAUISAURUS → 3 → 4

13

14

MEGALODON

18 → 19 → MAUISAURUS

FINISH

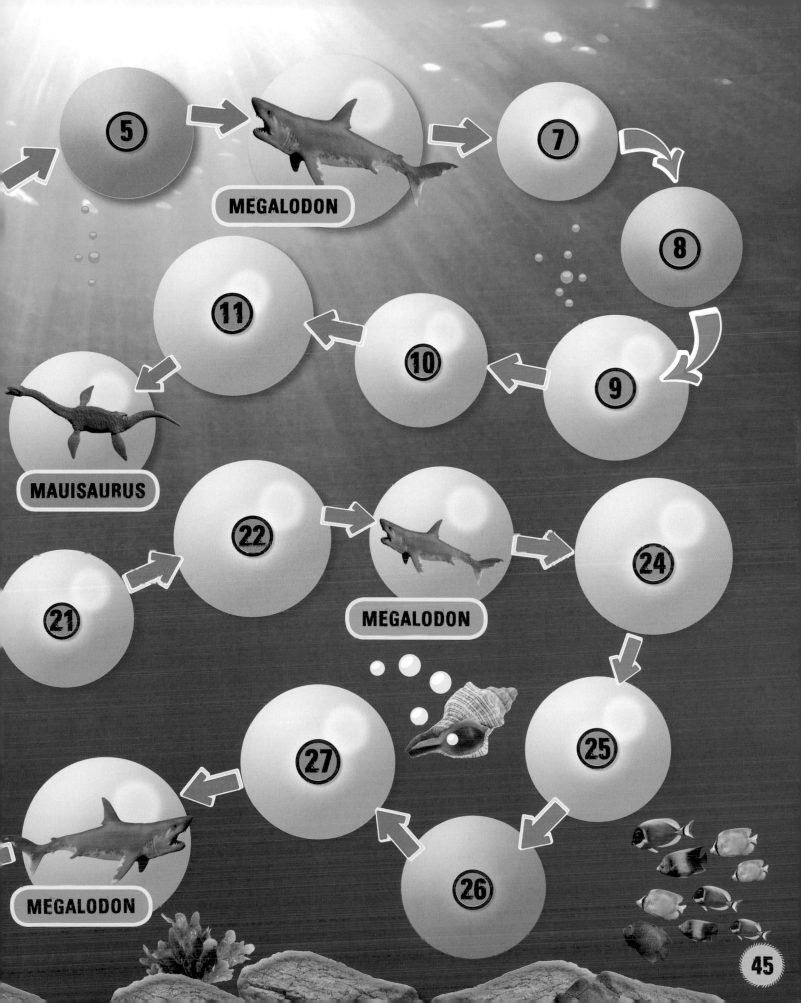

MEGALODON

MAUISAURUS

MEGALODON

MEGALODON

DEEP-SEA SUDOKU

Finish this grid using stickers from your sticker sheet. Each column and row should have only one of each creature.

ROWS

MONSTER MYSTERY

Use the clues below to work out which of these prehistoric sea monsters is being described.

Clues

The sea monster has:

1. Sharp teeth
2. Green areas of skin
3. A sharp fin on its back

Answers on page 48

LIOPLEURODON
(LIE-OH-PLOOR-UH-DON)

Period: Jurassic
203–135 million years ago

HEIGHT: 3m (10ft)
LENGTH: 11m (35ft)
WEIGHT:22,880kg(50,000lbs)

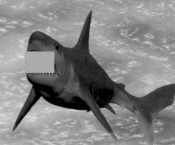

ANSWEr PAGE

Page 34:
Ocean Oddities: F

Page 34:
Jigsaw Jumble: 1-A, 2-E, 3-C, 4-D
Odd one out is B

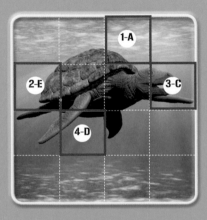

Page 36:
Liopleurodon Shadows: D
Creature Close-Up: A-2, B-3, C-4, D-1

Page 38:
Megalodon Maze:

Page 42:
Dunkleosteus Memory Test:
1-false, 2-true, 3-false, 4-true

Page 42:
Double Trouble: B-G, D-F, C-E
Odd one out is A

Page 43:
Find and Count: 11 Dunkleosteus,
14 Megalodon, 6 Sea Scorpion.

Page 46:
Deep-Sea Sudoku:

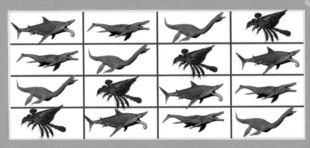

Page 46: Monster Mystery: C